AB...

Describes the cultiv...
seaweed 'crop', it...
culinary uses; and t...
kelp in alleviating ...
mucous colitis, and ...

Also by G. J. Binding
ABOUT COMFREY
ABOUT GARLIC
ABOUT POLLEN
ABOUT SOYA BEANS
ORGANIC GARDENING AND FARMING

Also by Alan Moyle
CONQUERING CONSTIPATION
DIETS TO HELP ACNE
DIETS TO HELP BRONCHIAL TROUBLES
DIETS TO HELP CATARRH
DIETS TO HELP CONSTIPATION
DIGESTIVE TROUBLES
NATURAL HEALING
SELF-TREATMENT FOR INSOMNIA
SLIMMING NATURALLY

ABOUT KELP

Seaweed for Health and Vitality

by

G.J. BINDING
M.B.E., F.R.H.S.

and

ALAN MOYLE
N.D., M.B.N.O.A.

THORSONS PUBLISHERS LIMITED
Wellingborough, Northamptonshire

First published 1974
Second Impression 1976
Third Impression 1977
Fourth Impression 1979
Fifth Impression 1984

© THORSONS PUBLISHERS LIMITED 1974

This book is sold subject to the condition that it shall not, by way of trade or otherwise, be lent, re-sold, hired out, or otherwise circulated without the publisher's prior consent in any form of binding or cover than that in which it is published and without a similar condition including this condition being imposed on the subsequent purchaser.

ISBN 0 7225 0256 7

Printed and bound in Great Britain by
Richard Clay (The Chaucer Press), Ltd.,
Bungay, Suffolk

CONTENTS

Chapter   *Page*

     Introduction   7
1. Seaweed — Oldest Crop in the World 9
2. Agricultural and Garden Uses 15
3. Seaweed Farming 22
4. Seaweed's Hidden Secrets 28
5. Putting Kelp on the Menu 32
6. Avoiding Confusion 36
7. The Respiratory System 40
8. Indigestion and Ulcers 43
9. Gastric Catarrh and Mucous Colitis 46
10. Gall Bladder Disease and Obesity 48
11. Constipation 51
12. Intestinal Disorders 53
13. Genito-urinary and Reproductive Systems 56
14. Musculo-skeletal and Neuro-muscular Systems .. 58
15. Other Uses 61

INTRODUCTION

Seaweed, though often considered more of a nuisance than anything else when decaying on our beaches is in fact one of the world's most remarkable plants. For centuries seaweed, was, and still is in some parts of the world used as a food for humans and animals. This plant from the seas now has a wide reputation as a garden fertilizer for use in horticulture and farming and more recently as a health supplement. Scientific evidence has supported ancient beliefs by confirming that seaweed contains large amounts of vitamins, minerals and trace elements. This humble plant can certainly prove a godsend in aiding a return to more natural gardening and farming methods.

It may come as a surprise that, even today, some 25 per cent of all food consumed in Japan consists of one form or another of sea-vegetable prepared and served in its many forms. Seaweed has been on the Japanese menu for centuries and is likely to remain a staple part of their diet.

As this book will show, there exists almost unlimited possibilities in our seas. Not only can vast amounts of natural gas be obtained but a constant supply of wholesome food from sea crops. In an ever-expanding world resources are being drastically reduced and land eroded. The water area of the world is many times that of the land space. In spite of over-fishing most seas remain relatively untapped and free from pollution. Sea farming in time could well prevent over-fishing and disputes over national fishing grounds. Talk of sea farming, like the old forecasts, decades ago, of visits to the moon, may be considered fantastic. In spite of this, by the turn of the century some scientists consider that the world's sea crops will have to be farmed to ensure the survival of our teeming populations.

Readers interested in studying this topic further should consult *Seaweed in Agriculture and Horticulture* by W.A. Stephenson (Faber and Faber).

CHAPTER ONE

SEAWEED – OLDEST CROP IN THE WORLD

Pliny the Elder referred to the use of seaweed in the first-century A.D. when compiling his *Natural History*. Today, as always, the Japanese are the foremost cultivators of crops, which play a vital role in their lives. Not only is every possible use of seaweed explored in Japan but it is also served as sea vegetables and comprises a major part of their total food supply. The ancient Chinese also thought highly of seaweed and made offerings of it as food to their ancestors. It was prized by the Romans as a manure and food for animals. The ancient Greeks are known to have used seaweed to treat intestinal disorders and counteract goitre, in spite of knowing nothing about iodine (seaweed is the world's richest source of this mineral, which greatly aids sufferers of goitre). In Japan during recent times a substance obtained from seaweed is being used to replace blood plasma, so often hard to obtain. This shows the close mineral content relationship between this sea crop and human blood.

Kelps
Kelps mainly consist of the larger algae which are olive/brown in colour. There are said to be over 800 species of these but for processing kelp tablets the *fucus vesiculosus* is most commonly used. The Pacific ocean is the home of the great kelps, some of which grow to over 500 feet in length.

The Kelp Industry
For a long time seaweed, or wrack as it was called, was burnt to obtain the mineral content. From the residue ash, bromine, iodine and potash could be extracted. This trade

became widespread in coastal regions and on the Scilly Isles the burning of kelp continued from 1684 till the nineteenth century. The name 'kelp' was at first used to refer to the ash formed, but as time went by it became another name for seaweed. Ash deposits up to two feet high or more could be recovered in trenches after dried seaweed had been burnt in special kilns. The ash from kelp is very rich in soda which, until other methods were found, was used in the manufacture of glass. Then when the kelp trade started to decline another boom took place after the French discovered that it contained a rich supply of iodine. So the same procedure was carried out to recover iodine and business in kelp prospered till cheaper ways of obtaining this mineral were discovered. The Japanese continued to use kelp for their supplies.

Alginic Acid

Again in 1883 kelp was given a new lease of life when Stanford discovered a way of obtaining what became known as alginic acid from this unusual sea crop. However the acid was not widely used for many years, until it was shown that transparent paper could be made from it. The alginic industry then really boomed for many other uses were discovered for this substance which included its use in many different industries. A list of the varied uses of alginates appears at the end of this chapter.

Agar-Agar

The word 'agar' was first used in Malaya to describe a red type of seaweed used in jelly making, 'agar-agar' in Malay meaning plurality. Until the entry of the Japanese into the 1939/45 war they processed the entire world's supply of agar-agar. This again shows how industrious they were in exploiting the wealth of the sea. With Japanese supplies being cut off, other countries experimented with seaweed and produced their own supplies of agar-agar.

Carrageenin

Some confusion exists between alginates and agar-agar, for they are somewhat related. In more recent years many of the uses of agar have been replaced by alginates. To mention carrageenin may only cause more misunderstandings so we briefly describe this product mainly obtained from red seaweeds and in particular from Irish moss. The carrageenin extracts are mainly used to make weaker jelly formations in such substances as milk, cocoa and chocolate.

Manure for Centuries

In spite of Western countries lagging behind in the East in making use of sea plants this has not always been the case. We have evidence that as long ago as the twelfth century seaweeds were used in Europe for manures. The Icelanders are an example of this, for, with limited crops available, even today seaweed is fed to all kinds of animals including cattle, horses and sheep apart from being used as a manure. In the Channel Islands and among Irish and Scottish farmers seaweed has played a role in farming for generations.

Without the average person being aware of the fact, even in England the consumption of seaweed slowly increases as more uses are found for this versatile plant. With a unique chemical content known as alginate it proves a boon to food manufacturers for soups, sauces, gravies, *glacé* cherries, jellies, custards and in the making of ice cream. One United Kingdom firm at one time produced 25 per cent of the world's alginates for external use in the textile trade. So kelp appears in many unsuspected forms every time our wives fill up their shopping baskets.

Seaweed is Here to Stay

Seaweed meal was produced in the U.S.A. at the turn of the century and in England during the first World War. Kelp for animal foods, as a manure, and to a lesser extent as a sea vegetable, is certainly not new to England. It was in 1920 that a certain Philip Park observed cattle bypassing grass pasture to graze on seaweed off the shore. Becoming fascinated, he investigated seaweed as a food, and this culminated in him producing crops for fodder.

In 1950 a Mr McInnes opened a factory at Nairn in Scotland for processing seaweed for both cattle food and as a fertilizer. Gradually it became accepted as a food supplement for chickens, horses, cattle, pigs, ewes and lambs.

Concentrated Seaweed

In spite of the use of seaweed for so long, even if for limited purposes, it was not until 1949 that events commenced which finally led to it being accepted as one of the finest fertilizers available. For this we must thank the perseverance of the late Mr W.A. Stephenson, whose untiring efforts finally resulted in the concentrated form of liquid seaweed taken so much for granted today. Today British seaweed extracts for feeding crops, and as valuable food for livestock, are sold in over forty countries.

In addition to liquid fertilizers there are many kelp products, including: tablets sold as a health food supplement; kelp powder for adding to dishes such as soups or other meals in the course of cooking; kelp skin food and seaflower toilet soap; not forgetting the sea vegetables mentioned in detail in Chapter Five. Other commercial uses include the use of seaweed in the making of toothpaste, puddings, blancmange, laver bread, synthetic cream. The Americans have got this cream-making off to a fine art for it has the appearance and taste of real cream. In Japan they even make seaweed flour.

Thalassotherapy

An organic revitalization spa known as 'Renaissance Spa' has been established in the beautiful Bahamas. At this spa a large bath is filled with sea water warmed to room temperature. Sea water is also sprayed over the entire body. Persons taking this treatment describe it as being like a most penetrating massage. There are special showers with lounge chairs placed in horizontal positions. Sea water is pumped through nozzles to give a fine massage over the entire body. It is believed that seaweed's minerals can be absorbed through the skin, and these are available in sea water. In England many hydros and beauty farms use seaweed extracts in baths for the treatment of rheumatic conditions. Rheumatism and arthritis sufferers benefit greatly from hot seaweed baths, which are also used in other treatments, including slimming. Seaweed is also used to make fine natural toilet soap. One such variety, containing all the goodness of this sea crop, has been aptly named 'Neptune's Bounty'.

Thousands of Species

It has been estimated that there are some 2,500 varieties of marine plants, all rich in minerals, trace elements and vitamins. So seaweed or kelp covers a great variety of plants of many hues, shapes and sizes.

One problem gradually being overcome in the business of seaweed is the high cost of producing the end product. Yields however can prove very high, being as much as 60 tons per acre. In Norway there is a vast sea farming industry and even before the last war some 67,000 tons were farmed annually. It was during the last war that necessity forced countries to turn to seaweed crop research. This applied in particular to the U.S.A. and this country.

Macrobiotic Food

Although to many people the very thought of eating seaweed meals may sound distasteful, seaweed is part of the macrobiotic cooking which is becoming very popular in America and Europe. A basic belief of followers is that one should mainly eat foods of the country in which they live. This of course refers to crops, fruits and vegetables. Well, apart from deserts and places hundreds of miles inland, kelp is available all over the world.

INDUSTRIAL USES OF ALGINATES

Industry	Used for	Product
Food and Bakery	Thickening	Filling Creams
		Lemon Curd
		Soups
Cosmetic	”	Toothpaste
		Hand creams
		Shampoos
		Lotions
Textile	”	Printing Paste
Rubber	”	Latex
Food and Bakery	Emulsifying Stabilizing	Ice cream
		Soft drinks
		Baker's emulsions
Pharmaceutical	”	Emulsions
General	”	Polishes
		Emulsion paints
		Welding electrodes
		Insecticides
Food and Bakery	Gelling and binding	Jellies
		Milk jellies
		Puddings
Pharmaceutical and Cosmetic	”	Tablets
		Hand and anti-burn lotions
Dental	”	Impression Powder
Medical	”	Haemostatics
Ceramics	”	Glazes and engobes
General	”	Sintered products

Food	Film and	Sausage casings
Pharmaceutical	filament forming	Barrier creams
Medical	"	Absorbent dressings
Textile	"	Soluble yarn
Paper	"	Transparent paper
General	"	Coated papers
		Washable wall paper
		Anti-stick and mould release agents
		Leather

CHAPTER TWO

AGRICULTURAL AND GARDEN USES

It is an accepted fact that our oceans are older than the land, so in all probability vegetation from the sea existed before any land plants. Seaweed is one of the oldest of manures, being very rich in potash and sea salts. With the advent of the Common Market and continued inflation increasing food prices almost weekly, people are again beginning to cultivate more of their own vegetables. Many are convinced that organic home grown produce is superior to mass produced crops from chemical farming. To supply liquid manures, sprays and feeds, makes for better vegetables with a natural flavour. Cultivators seeking an organic fertilizer will find seaweed products to be among the finest. Seaweed fertilizers greatly aid the grower in producing bumper crops more able to resist disease. In fact seaweed has been amply proved by tests over a long period to provide six advantages for crops and these are:

Increased seed germination.
Greater resistance against frost.
Assists plants to get more nutrients from the soil.
Builds up resistance to disease.
Builds up resistance to insect pests.
Prolongs the shelf life of such crops.

Extensive trials over many areas have shown seaweed

fertilizers ideal for every garden crop including flowers, fruit, vegetables, herbs, lawns, in fact everything that grows. Even lime-hating vegetables such as potatoes thrive on it. In fact seaweed provides maximum organic growth and protection for a minimum amount of work. It is a fine tonic and foliar feed, especially if sprayed on the underside of leaves. Any excess simply runs into the soil as a feed. With seaweed there is no danger of overfeeding.

Spraying of crops should be carried out in the early morning or late evening for at these times plants are able to absorb more nutrients. An important fact about seaweed is that it is perfectly safe for animals, humans and the soil. It will not harm birds, fish, worms, bees and all the multitude of insects and creatures which aid organic culture.

A Weed for Every Garden

Seaweed as a plant food has been used for generations, in fact, in coastal areas as long as man has tilled the land. In many parts of Devon, Cornwall, the Channel Islands, Ireland, Scotland and Brittany it is taken by farmers from the shore in the autumn, dried for composting with straw, or fed directly into the soil, and by spring a fine organic humus results. Many liquid seaweed supplements for organic gardeners are now available. These are clean, easy to use and very economical considering all the advantages.

Concerning supplies from our beaches, the finest type of seaweed for the gardener is the long variety with wide ribbons and crenellated edges. Another good one is the species with bladders, which young children like to pop. The small coloured varieties are the least suitable. Seaweeds cast up during the early spring and summer tides are more suited than those swept ashore in late summer and autumn. Seaweed should be carefully dried before use, under cover for best results, for it is then a finer plant food than it is in a wet state, needing only half the amount to produce the same yield. For example, 1 cwt of fresh

AGRICULTURAL AND GARDEN USES

seaweed is required for 6 square yards of soil, whereas ½ cwt of dry seaweed suffices for the same area.

Maritime plants such as spinach, tomatoes, sea-kale, asparagus, artichokes and so on, greatly benefit from feeds of seaweed.

Present-day chemical farming, coupled with the continuous use of insecticides, in the long run proves dangerous to soil structure and to rectify this seaweed offers unlimited possibilities. Since the advent of the chemical fertilizer, more gardeners than ever are again looking towards natural means of pest control and crop feeding. Its no longer considered old-fashioned to make use of all available plants, weeds and kitchen waste for compost making. The '1970 Conservation Year' made an impact which will remain for many gardeners, and organic growers are no longer considered cranks. Seaweed can play a vital role for farmer, smallholder or gardener, and by its application even depleted soils can be given a new lease of life in two years.

Compost Making

There are many ways of making natural compost heaps, since no less than twenty organic activators are available from animal manures and dried blood to fish meal and seaweed. For excellent results, economy and simplicity, seaweed as a compost activator rates second to none. The author averages between one and two — or even more — tons of vegetable waste, etc., throughout the year, and this is broken down to compost. Heaps can be activated by simply sprinkling a handful of powdered seaweed activator each time the heap is built up to about one foot in height. This makes for speedy and natural decomposition of all weeds and waste matter into friable, rich, dark-coloured organic compost. Extensive tests at The Henry Doubleday Research Association have conclusively shown that their seaweed activator will produce such results.

Persons able to obtain seaweed direct from the beaches,

(and as a glance will show, there is plenty about), can use it for activating heaps. However, it is advisable to first dry the weed, under cover, as it is then twice the strength and will not attract flies.

Review of Composting 1971

During this review, which took place at the Department of Chemical Engineering, University of Birmingham, it was established that of the eight organic substances used for composting, some 1,000,000 tons of seaweed was utilized annually in the United Kingdom. Although this is only a small amount by comparison with the other organic manures also studied, it is a move in the right direction. For all its useful purposes, seaweed is now firmly established in agriculture and horticulture and is here to stay.

'A Boost for Tired Soils'

An article with such a title appeared in the June 1973 issue of *The Soil Association Journal*. This introduced Fosmerl, an organic fertilizer consisting of gasfa phosphate from Tunisia and calcified seaweed (Maerl). The levels of manganese, iodine, calcium, sulphur and trace elements have been boosted in this organic fertilizer for even better results. The demand for this seaweed-based soil conditioner is such that a £4,000,000 factory has been specially built at St Malo in France for the sole purpose of producing Fosmerl. Farmers using it on their crops have reported excellent results. Today, with many growers changing to more natural methods, organic fertilizers will prove a boon in every possible way. Once again seaweed is being recognized for its ability to restore or retain soil fertility. In closing I would like to quote the final words from this article, which show that once again seaweed has proved its worth. 'A good farmer considers himself successful when he leaves the land in a better heart than he found it. Any farmer who uses fosmerl will do precisely

AGRICULTURAL AND GARDEN USES

that.' For the benefit of readers who are unaware of the Soil Association, it has world-wide membership and publishes Britain's leading journal on organic farming, gardening, wholefood and nutrition, market information for organic produce.

Healthy Live Stock

Grass of every kind in a dried or fresh state is used mainly for cattle fodder. The appearance of grass crops can be very deceptive and those lacking nitrogen and trace elements do not make good fodder. To feed with seaweed is a simple yet proved method of counteracting deficiencies in grassland for grazing.

Ground kelp is used as a livestock food in many parts of the world and for horses seaweed is added to their diet as a food supplement. Pigs fed on seaweed receive an increase in resistance to disease and produce litters with higher fertility rates. For poultry a seaweed supplement has an immediate effect on the health of birds, bringing increased egg supplies with more natural shells and deeper yolks. This also results in longer life for the birds with a reduced mortality rate. Another remarkable effect of seaweed is to put back into the egg some of the qualities that mass production has taken away. Many people are concerned about the chalky white shells and pale yolks of our battery egg supplies. Studies have proved that to add seaweed to chicken feed restores some of the natural properties of the diet to such an extent that the eggs have deeper yolks with the more natural shells of the free range hen. Cattle grazing on such land as the Channel Islands and on farms bordering the sea are disease-free, and if given the choice take seaweed by instinct.

Organic Husbandry

Farmers and gardeners can reap the benefits of seaweed's many uses to help produce natural crops. In this book the use of seaweed for the gardener, and its natural healing powers, can only be briefly introduced. It proves excellent for grass fodder and all vegetable crops. Abundant crops of disease and pest-free vegetables have been grown under controlled conditions using seaweed fertilizers. Giant sized marrows, pumpkins and onions are some of the vegetables displayed at vegetable shows. The chances are that growers have fed their exhibits with weekly doses of seaweed or liquid manure. The author has discovered this time and time again. A prize-winning potato grower for many years told his success story, which amounts to feeding his potatoes constantly with liquid seaweed. In 1954 the author took over a large allotment and during the ten years which followed liquid manures proved invaluable. When concentrated seaweed became available, this was used by many plot-holders with excellent results. At this time, in common with most people, I knew little or nothing about the amazing power of seaweed. Over the years the true facts have been revealed and amply substantiated. Seaweed is also used for bowling greens, orchards, fruit and hops. In fact, you name the crop and seaweed will supply the medium of growth; it is just as simple as that.

Seaweed and Manures

What is most remarkable is that seaweed contains all the goodness of farm-yard manure with the addition of vitamins, minerals and trace elements. It is perfectly clean, easy to handle and store. In concentrated liquid form it equals many times its own weight of farm-yard manure and as little as one teaspoonful makes one gallon of organic fertilizer.

Every crop needs some of the minerals and other elements available in seaweed for healthy growth. When it is applied to the land direct from the seashore, in its natural state — whether fresh or dry — decomposition must first occur before plants can assimilate the benefits. With concentrated liquid seaweed this is not so, for the elements are immediately available to all forms of plant life.

AGRICULTURAL AND GARDEN USES

Concentrated seaweed liquid fertilizers are now available all over the world. Trials using them have been made in many countries on a wide range of crops, all of which received benefits; some very great indeed.

An International Seaweed Symposium took place at Sapporo, Japan in August 1971, on 'The Effects of Aqueous Seaweed Extract as a Fertiliser Additive.' A brief summary of some of the findings shows that the organic gardener using seaweed has made a wise choice. In the case of crops of bananas, use of seaweed extracts resulted in bunches shooting 8½ weeks earlier than usual. In the case of tomatoes a single application of the extract increased the yield by about 20 per cent. Potato crops were higher, with more evenly sized vegetables. In the case of corn, within 10 days of the first application such plants were on an average 25 per cent taller, with broader leaves and thicker stalks. Later the other plants made good the gain of those treated with the seaweed extract. But a count of the ears of corn revealed 74 and 73 in the two control rows and 100 and 109 in the two rows fed with the extract. In the case of oranges all trees fed with seaweed showed small but consistent increases. In the shipping of oranges, losses were minimized by those gathered from the trees fed with seaweed extract, resulting in longer shelf life.

The object with any cultivation, whether it be a small vegetable plot or a large farm, is to harvest good, naturally-grown crops. To foliar-feed plants with liquid seaweed can serve many purposes, including this one. We have had ample proof, over the years, that foliar-feeding results in the highest possible yields and healthy crops.

CHAPTER THREE

SEAWEED FARMING

With one of the world's densest populations and a long coastline for the size of their country, the Japanese have for some time been experts in the art of sea farming. Teams of girls, all expert swimmers and skin divers, play a part in this form of cropping, which is also known as aqua-culture. These underwater farm labourers are specially trained and equipped to carry out the cutting of seaweed from cultivated beds off the seashores. The Japanese have a unique way of cooking sea vegetables, as they are termed, to preserve nutrition. In most countries, even those with long coastal areas, seaweed is largely neglected and not even thought of as a food. This is rather unfortunate, for being rich in protein, vitamins and minerals, this unusual crop has much to offer. The Japanese, on the other hand, do not just stop at seaweed for they also collect plankton for making soup cubes. Plankton is neither plant nor animal, being the lowest form of life, but, like kelp is rich in bodily needs and delicious into the bargain, as members of the famed Kontiki expedition testified.

Japan also exports large amounts of kelp throughout the Far East and to other parts of the world. Marine farmers sow seaweed spores and have a rotation system of cropping for conservation purposes. Another way they have of cultivating crops is by placing rocks into inshore sea waters which allows seaweed to take hold and grow. They also have a system of driving bamboo sticks into the sand in bays or river mouths and spores quickly cling to them. The bamboo canes are then withdrawn and transplanted to a cultivation area, when the young seaweed plants soon grow and can eventually be harvested. Nets are also used to catch spores and after over 300 years of sea farming there are some 70,000 fishermen-cum-farmers employed on this work in Japan.

Long-lived Villages

Some years ago scientists became interested in the population of Hizato situated in the Nagano province of Japan. Nearly 10 per cent of the villagers were over seventy years of age and a survey showed there were 250 per cent more seventy-year-olds than in any other Japanese village. After an extensive study the conclusion drawn was that the diet of the inhabitants of Hizato was a contributing factor towards their longevity. It is interesting to note that the food consumed by these villagers consisted of all manner of vegetables, especially soya beans, millet, barley, buckwheat, wholemeal flour and lastly, our seaweed — a vital source of vitamins and minerals. In Hizato dried seaweed is available in its many forms and always consumed as part of the diet. Such varieties include *tangle, wakame,* (lobe leafed) and *hajiti.* Another species called *tengusa* was prepared as a form of gelantine. These village dwellers give a boost to vegetarianism for, being mostly Buddists, they rarely consume animal flesh.

Japan 1972

Dr Shewell-Cooper, one of the world's leading experts on organic husbandry, was invited to Japan during 1972 to give talks to members of the country's Ministry of Agriculture. He was very impressed with their seaweed farming and use of crops as a manure on farms and gardens, and was surprised to find that some 25 per cent of all Japanese foods consisted of kelp in one form or another. He and his wife were served with appetizing Japanese sea vegetable dishes including *komba,* and *nori,* or laver bread. *Wakami* was prepared as a vegetable dish and served for breakfast with *miso* soup. *Hiziki,* a darker crop, was sun dried, shredded and used as a vegetable. Agar was prepared in salads and used as a dessert. Dr Shewell-Cooper also found that the brown seaweeds were used in flour, for noodles, toasted or served with rice meals or in soups; some varieties of kelp he found were used for flavouring or sweetening beverages or played a part in the baking of cakes.

Norway

Seaweed is harvested in a number of countries with suitable coastlines and in Europe the main crops appear on Western coasts adjacent to the Gulf Stream. Some of the finest comes from Norway, where seaweed farming is well established. In fact Norway is probably second only to Japan in the art of aqua-culture. Other regions where crops are grown include France, parts of England, Ireland and Scotland, Portugal, Spain.

A species known as *ascophyllum* is the main variety cultivated by the Norwegians, who gather crops during high tide using shallow-bottomed boats. Some craft employ mechanically operated shears but other farmers still harvest crops by means of hand cutters. During gathering at least six inches of plant is left intact on the rocky formations to promote further growth. These crops, known as *asco*, are extraordinarily slow-growing, taking three years to reach maturity after harvesting. Conservation greatly depends on allowing plants to continue growing and not subject them to low, continuous cutting. Indiscriminate harvesting will gradually destroy a crop.

Collection and Drying

On being cut, sections float to the surface where they are gathered by means of nets or collected on rafts towed behind boats. Harvested crops are despatched direct to the factories for drying and grinding, or other processing. It is most important for crops to be harvested without delay, for once cut seaweed, in common with many other rare plants, soon starts to deteriorate. Such speedy procedure harnesses all the vitality of the living plants. The treatment of crops is an entirely natural process, nothing being removed or added to the seaweed. Drying takes place at low temperatures to avoid overheating. After grinding, the resultant meal is the finest olive green in colour. Only the best part of any harvest is reserved solely for the production of kelp tablets and seaweed powder, the bulk of all crops being utilized for animal feeds.

Liquid Fertilizer

The next stage, equally simple, consists of converting seaweed powder into a concentrated liquid fertilizer for crops, lawns, flowers — in fact all that grows. An extract from seaweed powder is obtained by steaming it in water under pressure; this again being an entirely natural process, nothing being added except a stabilizer to prevent fermentation. The resulting end-product consists of a rich dark brown liquid loaded with vitamins, minerals and trace elements from the fresh crops. Seaweed has been proved to be an amazing natural fertilizer which will produce bumper crops. This is because of its unspoilt, live content of organic vitamins, minerals and trace elements in the exact form nature intended them. It is of interest to know that the mineral content of *asco* equals three times that of any land plant — so rich and full of vitality, in fact, that over sixty elements have been identified. One may well ask, from where does all this goodness come? It has been leached from the soil by the elements of frost, snow, ice, storms and rainfall, and conveyed by brooks, streams and rivers out to sea. In the seas these minerals continue the never-ending process of life in feeding all forms of marine life, including hungry seaweed. Thus one of the finest ways of replacing the earth's mineral content and keeping or restoring a natural organic soil in the sphere of agriculture or gardening, is by using seaweed products on the land, or the plants in their fresh state. The chain of plant life is completed by providing such minerals as calcium, magnesium, iodine, iron, phosphates, potash and a mass of other vital, if minute properties, nowadays all known and proved to be important for vegetation, animals and plant life. So from the land via rivers to the sea and a return to the land through the medium of seaweed makes a complete, natural and health-giving cycle.

Britain

Britain, like Japan, is a small country with an extensive coastline. A survey carried out in recent years proved that our seashore provides some of the finest beds of seaweed anywhere in the world. Excellent crops appear in the English Channel and off the Welsh, Northumberland and Scottish coasts. The most prolific growth of this strange crop is in the area around the Hebrides and Orkney Islands and along the west coast of Scotland. As long ago as the sixteenth century in many parts of South Wales, seaweed taken in by the spring tides was conveyed on horses and carts as a manure for farmers.

Sea Lettuce

Sea lettuce or laver, as it is called, resembles spinach but contains a distinct oyster flavour like another rare vegetable, *salsify*, sometimes known as vegetable oyster. Laver can easily be gathered on the Devon, Cornish or Welsh coasts at low tide. It makes a nutritious and appetizing meal when served fried with bacon and eggs or some other breakfast dish, as it still is in many parts of Wales, even today.

Sea Vegetables in England

One may well assume that we are a long way behind the Japanese in putting kelp on the menu, but sea vegetables are available in England. By a coincidence, whilst getting details for this book, one of my daughters prepared what proved to be a delicious-tasting though somewhat mysterious dinner. Imagine my surprise, afterwards, when

SEAWEED FARMING

examining the packets of foodstuffs used, to find one of the main ingredients to be food from Japan, 'Hiziki Sea Vegetable' or seaweed in a dried form. It appears there are four such foods marketed in a dried package form by a London firm which are:

Wakame   Used mostly for soups and salads.
Hiziki   Prepared on its own as a main dish.
Konbu   Like soya sauce, used to enhance the flavour of soups and stocks.

All these meals originate from Japan, the fourth being *Dulse*, from Ireland, which can be served as a main dish or used to bring flavour to casseroles or salads.

The World's Largest Larder

Seaweed, in one form or another, has been used as a food for generations, so long, in fact, that mention was made of it in a Chinese book of poetry in 800 B.C. Seaweed, in its many forms, was considered by the Chinese and some other races as a delicacy. What ground can there be for assuming that in the vast oceans and seas in general, and, in seaweed in particular, we have the greatest food supply in the world? Well, experts on studying this strange crop have estimated that in the Sargossa sea alone the quantity of seaweed is so great as to be able to provide food for the entire population of Europe for 500 years. If treated kindly the seas will repay man great dividends for the supply of crops from underwater farming are practically inexhaustible. Such kind of farming cannot suffer drought, loss of crops through pests and diseases, needs no planting, weeding, feeding, spraying and is free from most other problems facing the farmer with crops on land.

Sea Farming and World Food Shortage

The future of seaweed as a crop will be uncertain till persons in authority and public opinion accepts the findings of scientists that we can obtain nutritious valuable supplies of food from the sea. At present, a very small quantity — which has been estimated at only about 1 per cent of the total world's food supply — comes from the sea. But there are signs that things are changing, for after centuries of ignorance concerning the value of the seas, man is at last — through necessity — looking to the sea for increased supplies of food. This action will, undoubtedly, in time greatly help solve the ever-increasing shortage of foods, especially of a protein content, caused by drought, over-population and all the other problems with which the world is faced. Meanwhile, seaweed is firmly established as one of the finest organic fertilizers in the world, being second to none.

CHAPTER FOUR

SEAWEED'S HIDDEN SECRETS

Minerals galore would be an apt way of describing maritime plants, which are ten or more times richer in these than any known crop growing on land. An attraction about these minerals is that they are in a natural state of biological balance. This is an important factor for excesses could prove harmful. When using seaweed as a fertilizer it is virtually impossible to give overdoses, especially in poor soils. The use of seaweed on the land often brings remarkable results. Also it presents an opportunity for organic gardeners and others concerned with the effects of pollution to restore vitality and goodness in a completely natural way with no adverse effects.

Iodine
Every mineral contained in the sea also appears in normal healthy human blood. Those lacking a vital bloodstream can derive benefits from sea food, especially seaweed, which alone can replace any deficiencies. A remarkable fact is that the sea is the richest source of supply of iodine. All

sea plants and creatures contain iodine, which is known to exert a tremendous influence on the body. The iodine content of kelp is apt to fluctuate in different parts of the world and during the seasons, as do other minerals slightly. What is miraculous is that the iodine content of any seaweed can be as much as 20,000 times more than that of the sea water in which the plants grew.

The Thyroid Gland

In 1882 a French doctor made the discovery that an intake of iodine would correct goitre, often present among communities far from coastal regions. In such places crops cultivated were very low or totally deficient in iodine. This substance has such remarkable power that one tiny drop in a glass of fruit juice overcomes stress and aids relaxation. What few crops contain iodine are those which for generations have grown near the sea. These include sea kale, tomatoes, spinach, artichokes and celery. This mineral serves another vital purpose when, like an army, it protects the blood stream by killing off invading germs. This gland also uses iodine to create a good crop of hair, so, this mineral is important for a healthy body and greatly helps warding off old age.

Many vitamins, trace elements and minerals have recently been discovered in kelp which indicate quite clearly why it has proved such a tonic and healer for hundreds of years.

The sugar content of seaweed is termed mannitol, which is not sweet enough to cause increase in blood sugar. This makes sea vegetables an ideal food for diabetics. Kelp is an excellent source of vitamins including vitamin A, B_{12} vitamin C, thiamine, riboflavin, niacin, pantothenic acid and vitamin D, to name a few. Very few land crops possess the ability to extract vitamin B_{12} from the soil. The author is aware of only two, namely comfrey and alfalfa. The richest source of vitamin B_{12} is liver. So all non-flesh eaters need sea vegetables, or such herbs as comfrey, included in their diet. Vitamin B_{12} tablets are available from Health Food Stores. In all, kelp contains 13 vitamins, 20 essential amino acids and 24 trace elements — quite formidable for a plant classed as a weed. As the most outstanding maritime crop it harnesses all the minerals from the sea. In fact the ash (mineral) content of seaweed is known to vary from 10 per cent to the enormous 50 per cent (ash is best described as the indestructible mineral content which still remains, even after burning the weed).

Foliar Feeding

Perhaps the most outstanding thing about a liquid seaweed concentration for the gardener is its ability to be able to feed plants through their leaves. This kind of feeding can serve many purposes. The main object with a garden, whether it be the smallest vegetable plot or thousands of acres, is to raise a good disease-free crop. Foliar feeding by spraying liquid seaweed extract will do just this with greatly increased yields. The reason is that plants are able to get a higher percentage of trace elements by this method of feeding. Foliar feeding also results in a better quality harvest and enhanced appearance in the case of fruit and vegetables. Furthermore such feeding creates a resistance to both pests and diseases and allows all growing things to obtain greater amounts of other nutrients from the soil. In many parts it was shown that foliar feeding considerably increased storage life of crops.

Scientific Proof

What proof is there that seaweed will perform such feats as feeding crops through their leaves, one may well ask? Nearly 100 years ago it was discovered that plant metabolics could be leached out during rainfall. It was therefore assumed that the reverse was possible, e.g., that crops could be fed via their leaves. Tests using flourescent liquids proved this to be a reality and further tests established the kind of nutrients available and utilized by plants through foliar feeding.

Kelp and Radioactivity

Can kelp act as a preventative measure against some of the dangers of the Atomic Age? Recent events would tend to suggest it can. At the McGill University, Montreal, Canada, Pacific-harvested kelp was shown to have some remarkable ability to reduce radioactive strontium 90 which persons had taken through their intestines by up to 80 per cent. The fact that seaweed has the power to do this was also confirmed by a Medical Research Radiological Unit at Harwell.

When we examine the average content of kelp — not including vitamins — there is perhaps every reason for concluding it can well have a power little short of miraculous.

AVERAGE CONTENTS OF KELP

This table refers to an analysis by the Norwegian Institute of Seaweed Research

Components	per cent	Carbohydrates	per cent
Proteins	5.7	Mannitol	4.2
Fat	2.6	Alginic Acid	26.7
Fibre	7.0	Methylpentosans	7.0
Nitrogen-free extracts	58.6	Laminarin	9.3
Moisture	10.7	Unidentified sugars	14.4
Ash	15.4		
	100.0		

On this analysis 60 different elements were also traced in seaweed, including minerals. Some of them were only very minute indeed but the fact is they were present. Such a large number of minerals and other elements must in no small way account for the power of this weed from our seas, which in tonnage must exceed the weight of any land crop.

CHAPTER FIVE

PUTTING KELP ON THE MENU

We have explored very briefly the history and uses of seaweed in gardening and agriculture. The use of seaweed in its various forms for every plant, flower or crop, is a vast subject which only growers themselves can continue to follow. This part of the book would not be complete, however, without some mention of the manner in which seaweed — kelp — or more appetizingly, sea vegetables, are likely to play an increasing role in dwindling world food supplies.

It is an accepted fact that — generally — English people are inclined to be cautious in trying foods from the East or even European countries. An exception is in the case of Chinese foods, which have become very popular, with restaurants opening all over the country. Many Chinese dishes include bean sprouts, which are both appetizing and enjoyable to most people. Although lovers of bean sprouts would probably hesitate to sample the soya bean, such sprouts are derived from the soya or mung bean. Also from China we have soy sauce, a most popular addition for enhancing many meals, which is another product of the bean. Many might consider that a diet in which kelp appeared would be like eating frogs' legs or partaking of some other unusual feast. So to try and clarify matters we now put before you the 'Kelp Menu', showing sea vegetables available in England and many other countries today. No doubt — like Chinese food — kelp will become more acceptable in the course of time. People understandably object to eating something they mostly see decaying on beaches, but they may be more inclined to sample 'kelp', which sounds more appetizing. Doubts may also disappear when it is revealed that such sea vegetables are cultivated under the most hygenic conditions, in unpolluted seas, by 'aqua farmers' whose ancestors have grown such crops for generations. Once eaten and enjoyed, kelp can become just as popular as Chinese food, of which it is a part. You may not be aware of the fact that Chinese bird's-nest soup has a kelp content, being prepared from nests built by swallows from dried seaweeds. In exploring these kelp dishes you are in for a pleasant surprise and any prejudices, such as those against Chinese food, invariably prove unfounded.

Kelp foods now available in dried package form include the five described here, four of which are from Japan and the other from Ireland. Make sure that any kelp foods you purchase are from reputable sources such as restaurants or shops serving macrobiotic foods. However, like most repasts, much depends upon what takes place in the kitchen and kelp is no exception to this, so attention to detail is important.

Here we take a look at our kelp dishes, with instructions for preparing and serving to provide tasty food in its most nutritious form.

RECIPES

Hiziki This type of kelp can be easily identified by the long thin strands, which are almost black in colour.
Kombu Consists of a greener species of kelp with a rather leathery appearance which is inclined to swell on being cooked.
Wakame Is a kelp sold in the form of sprouts or bunches or processed into thin sheets.
Nori This type of kelp is also prepared and sold in thin sheets.
Kanten Mostly used to thicken desserts; is a form of agar-agar with all its varied uses.
Dulse Here we have a type of kelp very similar to *hiziki*, except that it also bears some leaves (or seaweed's equivalent of leaves) as well as strands.

Hiziki
1 packet of *hiziki* kelp (for 4 servings), 2 small onions or

shallots, (if required), 1-2 teaspoons of oil (vegetable), water.
Rinse strands in cold water to remove any grains of sand, which even with the most careful harvesting may remain with the kelp. Place the strands in a bowl and cover completely with water and allow them to soak for about 15 minutes. Squueze out excess water, which should be retained. Chop up the strands to about 1-inch lengths. Heat up vegetable oil in a skillet, add chopped strands and *sauté* over high flame for about 2 minutes. If you desire to use small onions or shallots, slice them thinly, add to the skillet and in this case *sauté* with the *hiziki* strands for 5 minutes. Remove from heat and carefully pour the residue of the water over the kelp, retaining a small amount in the bowl. The remaining water should be discarded as it may well contain small particles of foreign matter, in no way harmful but with which the oceans are teeming. Now bring to the boil, cover — leaving an air gap — and simmer for about 25 minutes or until water has almost completely evaporated. If desired, two tablespoons or more of tamari may be added to taste just before cooking is finished.

For variety after preparation, *hiziki* may be served with roasted sunflower or sesame seeds, almonds or peanuts. Unlike many dishes, *hiziki* is enhanced by keeping in a refrigerator and tastes even better. It is delicious served with salads and rice, or it can be used in place of stuffing.

Kombu

There are many kinds of *kombu*, the most popular being *dashi*, *nato* and *torro*. The *dashi* kind is sold in fairly thick sheets, *nato* is prepared in thin strips or strands, not unlike *hiziki*. *Torro* is rather powdery and may be added direct to soups just before serving, needing no cooking or soaking beforehand. You will observe that various brands of kelp powder are available in Health Food Stores, and can be used for this purpose.

Kombu sautéed

After washing sufficient *nato kombu* in cold water, allow it to soak for 10 minutes in cold water. Squeeze out excess water and *sauté* in 1-2 teaspoonsful of vegetable oil for 10 minutes. If desired, a finely chopped raw carrot or onion, or both, may be added and *sautéed* with the kombu. Then season with *tamari* to taste and simmer for a further 10 minutes. Serve hot.

Dashi kombu can be substituted for *nato* in this recipe but in this case it should be cut into pieces 1-inch by ½-inch.

The *dashi kombu* being used may have been previously boiled to form a stock or soup.

PUTTING KELP ON THE MENU

Wakame

Generally *wakame* may be prepared and served in the same manner as *hiziki* but with this kind of kelp we also have sprouts and bunches. These, after washing in cold water, may have any tough centre stems removed and cooked as for *hiziki*.

Wakame with Onions

Dried *wakame* (up to 2ozs), 2 medium sized onions or 4 shallots, 3 Umeboshi plums (shredded).

After washing the *wakame*, allow it to soak in cold water for about 15 minutes and then strain off the water. Pour water slowly into saucepan, discarding the last small amount to dispose of any deposits. Finely chop onions (or shallots). Bring water to the boil, add chopped onion (or shallots), and allow to simmer for 2-3 minutes. Chop up *wakame* and add it to the water, cooking it for 5 minutes. Add shredded plums and simmer for a further 5 minutes.

Nori and Rice Balls

Nori and *wakame* are two rather similiar sea vegetables, except that *wakame* appears also in sprouts or bunches (like our watercress). So in many dishes *nori* or *wakame* can be used with similar results.

6 Sheets of *nori* or *wakame* kelp, 3 cups of rice (just cooked), 3 Umeboshi salt plums, a mixture of 5 per cent sea salt to cold water in a bowl.

Toast the sheets of kelp under a grill until they become crisp and cut each plum in half. Dip your hands in a bowl of water and shake off loose drops. Take about ½ a cup of rice at a time and mould it into a ball. Make holes in all the balls, large enough to insert the pieces of plum in the centre. Having done this press the rice around to cover the holes. Now wrap a sheet of kelp around each ball. For storing the rice balls use wax paper, not a sealed container, as the latter is apt to cause the rice to turn sour. Rice balls are very frequently prepared in the East for picnics, lunches, and make a snack for every occasion. If stored in wax paper they will keep for many days without being put in a refrigerator.

CHAPTER SIX

AVOIDING CONFUSION

One of the most confusing things about seaweed is the various names by which it is generally termed. Thus it is possible for names like seaweed, kelp, Irish moss, Iceland moss, carrageen, dulse, laver, agar-agar, etc., to be used. What must be realized, however, is that seaweed varies, not only from one geographical region to another, but also from the season when it is collected. Seaweeds are the plant life of the sea and come under the group of plants known as *algae* and are some of the earliest members of the plant world. It is probably one of the few members of plant life which has remained unchanged for centuries, since its cultivation and growth is still largely controlled by the elements — not man.

Rich in Iodine

The protein, vitamin and mineral content of edible seaweed can vary from region to region. The 'gelling' properties of seaweeds also vary. All edible seaweeds, however, are rich in iodine and trace elements gathered from the sea. Seaweeds grow on rocks on the sea-bed and do not, like land plants, have roots in the normal sense. Seaweed attaches itself to rocks with tentacles called *holdfasts* and the plants feed directly on sea water and have the capacity of storing and concentrating the protein, carbohydrate, vitamins and mineral salts in the leaves and stems of the plant.

Algae are classified into four principal groups:

Green algae	=	Chlorophyceae
Brown algae	=	Phaeophyceae
Red algae	=	Rhodophyceae
Blue-green algae	=	Cyanophyceae

AVOIDING CONFUSION

It is the brown and the red algae that are the principal seaweeds involved in food and as therapeutic agents.

In the northern hemisphere it is the brown seaweeds that pre-dominate, although red seaweed can be seen at the low water-mark. The names applied to seaweed of the common *fucus* varieties are bladderwrack, kelp, seaweed, kelpware and fucus. It is this variety, together with *Macrocystes Pyrifera* and *Ascophyllum Nodsum,* which are used in seaweed tablets and bath preparations, etc. In actual fact, however, there are quite a number of edible seaweeds used as food and medicine. Even some of the green seaweeds are used as food.

The true Irish moss is a red seaweed from the Chondrus variety of seaweed. These and other similar seaweeds grow either at the low watermark or under the grown seaweeds. A different type of red seaweed, gathered in spring and summer is known as laver or sloke in England and Wales, as slack in Scotland and in Ireland as sloke. This is the extremely tasty type of edible seaweed. Dulse is another specimen of edible red seaweed.

On the Pacific coast of America, a large brown seaweed, closely related to the brown seaweeds around British coasts, is known as kelp. A similar type of large brown seaweed is the giant bull kelp. Seaweeds vary in their distribution around the world. In the cold-water zones it is the large brown seaweeds which pre-dominate, though the red seaweeds are found. In the central warm-water areas the red seaweeds are in preponderance and in the southern temperate and cold-water zones considerable quantities of both brown and red seaweed are to be found.

Seaweed as a Food Supplement

Seaweed or kelp tablets are now familiar food supplements. These can be produced from a variety of seaweeds, including *Fucus Vesiculosis, Ascophyllum Nodsum* and *Macrocystes Pyrifera.* Bath preparations are made from seaweeds such as dulse, tangle and bladderwrack.

Confusion can be avoided if it is recognized that all seaweeds, when used as food supplements, may be simply called either seaweed tablets, kelp tablets or possibly another name commencing or ending with *algae*. The latter, of course, is a reference to all seaweed plants.

Seaweed as a food supplement is a relatively new approach. Agar-agar and carrageen or Irish moss have been used therapeutically for many years. Despite the longer history of both forms of seaweed, many practitioners — allopathic and naturopathic — failed to recognize the value of both these primitive forms of seaweed. The fact that carrageen was used in the First World War appears to have escaped notice, though agar-agar has been in vogue in one form or another as a laxative for many years. To avoid confusion it is possible to apply three names to Carrageen moss. These can be simply carrageen moss, Irish moss or Iceland moss. The most familiar term, however, is carrageen moss. In the following pages, therefore, the terms *carrageen moss* only will be employed when referring to this type of seaweed.

Agar-agar is used as a food agent, preservative, commercially in industry and, of course, therapeutically as a laxative. Agar-agar was first produced in China and it was around 1662 that it was introduced in Japan. Over thirty seaweeds, principally in the Southern hemisphere — especially Japan — are involved in the production of agar-agar. The seaweeds which make up agar products have variously been known as Japanese isinglass, Japanese gelatine, etc., but agar-agar is now the accepted term.

When seaweed is used as a direct food it will be called either *sloke, laver* or *dulse,* if it is actually produced in the British Isles. If it is imported, however, the names would be *Hiziki, Kombu, Wakmai* or *Nori.*

Agar-agar is principally used in food technology and chemistry and as a laxative. In the food industry it is sought after for its 'gelling' qualities, as a thickening agent and preservative. It can, like carrageen moss, be used for making jellies. Agar-agar, however, has many medicinal properties similar to carrageen, and can be used as a laxative, or for treating menstrual disorders.

Carrageen for Chest Conditions

Carrageen moss has an even more important place in therapeutics than agar-agar. Like agar-agar it possesses great 'gelling' properties. In Great Britain the standard set down as the 2.5 g. of moss heated with 100 ml. of water will give a firm jelly on cooling. Carrageen moss is extensively employed in food preparations (especially for binding and thickening) and in the textile and other industries. Most of the vegetable jellies, blancmanges and moulds are prepared from 'bleached' carrageen moss. Carrageen moss replaced gelatine, which was in short supply, during the last war. Unbleached carrageen moss contains greater 'gelling' qualities since no 'gelling' material has been washed out in its preparation. This unbleached moss is advised in all chest conditions. Carrageen moss can be obtained in its more natural and primitive state. In this case it is merely washed, cleaned and dried and nothing is removed. The prepared and bleached moss, while still an extremely valuable food product, does lose a little of its effectiveness as a therapeutic agent, particularly in the treatment of respiratory conditions.

CHAPTER SEVEN

THE RESPIRATORY SYSTEM

Millions of hours of study and work are lost every winter because of the common cold and influenza. Nasal catarrh, laryngitis and catarrhal deafness are all-the-year-round afflictions. But bronchitis, emphysema and asthma are the serious respiratory complaints which affect so many. Sufferers from bronchitis and emphysema, in particular, dread the cold and damp of the winter.

Adverse climatic conditions undoubtedly aggravate respiratory complaints. Damp and cold play such a part in raising the incidence of respiratory troubles that too many people tend to blame everything on the weather. In the case of colds, infection is added to climatic conditions as the major cause of the ailment. Infection, like weather, is an over-subscribed aspect of the common cold and takes too little regard of the natural immunity a healthy body can acquire.

The symptoms of a common cold are familiar enough: headache, sneezing, coughing, nasal catarrh, raised temperature, shivering, etc. True, the cold can be triggered off by a combination of a chill, subjection to damp or draught, close contact with people who sneeze or a variety of adverse factors. At the same time, however, the body's defences must be in a weak state before a cold develops and, once developed, the system uses the cold as a means of discarding accumulated waste matter.

When a cold develops the appetite is lost and the slight feverishness points to a burning up of waste matter and the 'running nose' and sneezing is nature's attempt to expel the excess mucus. The natural reaction to a cold, or to any acute disease, is loss of appetite. This is a safeguard. The body is occupied with eliminating waste products and while it has neither the energy nor desire for food, the need for liquid is increased.

Seaweed Assists Bowel Movements

The cure for a cold, therefore, is rest, warmth and ample fluids. These fluids should be clear vegetable soups and diluted fruit juices. The soups can be slightly thickened with carrageen moss and it should be added to all fruit juices. Though a cold can cause diarrhoea, the opposite is usually the case and a previous history of constipation and catarrh is often found when colds are prevalent with some people. The seaweed, apart from its direct healing effect, assists normal bowel movements.

Bronchitis is often called 'the English disease' — and not without reason, considering how prevalent it is, especially during the winter months. It has been estimated that 26 million working days are lost in Britain because of bronchitis. Anything, therefore, that helps to prevent this loss is worth considering. What is more important, however, is to prevent the suffering it entails.

Bronchitis not Inevitable

Bronchitis is not inevitable. Serious attention must be paid to diet, posture and correct breathing. At the same time as many irritants as possible should be avoided. What is unfortunate is that in the average case it is mainly the symptoms which are treated. Even then, the symptoms are usually suppressed by drugs, which supply relief but do not cure. Antibiotics are too often the ready answer to bronchitis. All drugs, and antibiotics are no exception, have side-effects.

The frequent recurrence of bronchitis, especially during the winter months, demonstrates the failure of treating symptoms and ignoring the cause. When respiratory mucous membrane is continually bombarded with irritants, or the diet contains an excess of mucus-forming and acid food, then bronchitis will recur with increasing frequency during inclement weather. The only way to avoid bronchitis is to amend the diet, reduce direct and indirect irritants to delicate mucous membrane and establish good patterns of posture and breathing. Any restriction to movements of the rib cage from defective posture, shallow breathing or reduction in spinal mobility must be rectified.

Seaweed and Garlic

Two essentials in the diet for those with a tendency to respiratory ailments — and this includes emphysema and asthma — are seaweed and garlic. Both can be taken as food supplements in tablet or capsule form. Seaweed, however, should also be regularly included in the diet as a direct food or drink. Carrageen moss can be used in conjunction with vegetable soup or fruit juice to make a slightly gelatinous drink or in the form of sweet or savoury jellies. A practical recommendation is to have a fruit drink with carrageen moss added last thing at night and to keep a flask of the mixture by the bedside in case it is required during the night. If not used, it can then be taken first thing in the morning. It can be prepared as follows:

    1 pint water
    ¼ oz Carrageen moss
    Juice and rind of one lemon and orange
    Honey to taste.

The above recipe is for the carrageen moss in its natural form — i.e., as dried seaweed. The ingredients can be simmered for a few minutes and then strained, if a quick drink is required. An alternative method is to pour the hot water on to the carrgeen, juice and rind and leave it to stand for a few hours. Sweetening may then be added when the drink, by that time slightly gelatinous, is strained and served.

While seaweed is strongly recommended for its therapeutic properties, it is inadvisable for any person with a proclivity to respiratory troubles just to take it in times of

illness. Everyone can gain by using seaweed as a regular item of diet, but it should never be forgotten that the carragean moss drink increases resistance to irritants of mucous membrane and helps prevent respiratory diseases.
In addition it supplies an alkaline medium essential for the entire body, plus natural vitamins.

CHAPTER EIGHT

INDIGESTION AND ULCERS

Mucous membrane lines the alimentary tract and is very subject to irritation. The two main enemies of the digestive system are catarrh and excessive acidity. Both have a common ground in faulty nutrition in that an excessive intake of mucus-forming food almost automatically infers an excess of acids in the system, since all mucus-forming food is also acid-forming. Other factors, of course, especially excessive use of aspirin-type drugs, come into the picture, but diet is of paramount importance.

Dyspepsia and excess of acidity is bound to arise when the diet contains too much fried food, pickles, sauces, condiments and rich food of any type. Simplicity in food is one of the surest means of avoiding the digestive upsets that attack so many people. Unfortunately over-indulgence, unwise as it may be, is a prevalent weakness. But dietetic indiscretions have to be paid for at one time or another. When such indiscretions are too frequent, and especially when they are combined with 'stress' conditions, onset of ulcers is only a matter of time.

Seaweed an Alkaline Food

Acidity can arise from tension, irritability and nervous exhaustion. The habit of bolting food does not help good digestion, nor does bad posture, which cramps the abdominal organs. Acidity is reduced when the alkaline elements in diet (leafy and root vegetables, fresh and dried fruit) are increased. Seaweed must be added to the list of alkaline foods.

Iodine is not solely a gland regulator. A deficiency of iodine contributes to digestive troubles. Chlorine and potassium are well represented in seaweed. Chlorine is necessary for the production of hydrochloric acid to ensure the digestion of proteins and acts on the liver to assist it in removing poisons from the system. Chlorine is the cleansing agent. Potassium is a regulator of the normal contraction and relaxation of muscles, thereby assisting the peristaltic movements of the colon and helping to prevent both constipation and diarrhoea. Potassium, together with sodium (also contained in seaweed) play a large part in ensuring alkalinity and preventing catarrh and the formation of stones in the gall-bladder, kidneys and urinary bladder.

Gastric and duodenal ulcers arise when excessive acidity creates an intensive inflammatory process in the mucous membrane, which involves the death of minute portions of that tissue and breaks the continuity of the tissue. Stress plays a great part in the formation of an excessive flow of hydrochloric acid. The normal acid content of the gastric juices does not cause ulceration. When, however, an excess of acid in the diet and other irritants (smoking, toxic matter inhaled from sprays, etc.), attack the mucous membrane, conditions are ripe for the formation of a gastric or duodenal ulcer.

Chlorine is necessary for the production of hydrochloric acid, but it is also the 'cleaner' of the body and would not, in itself, be responsible for an excess of hydrochloric acid in the digestive juices. The balance in the mineral content of the body is dependent upon a sufficient intake of the alkaline elements in diet. When this rule of alkalinity is observed, no excess of acid (providing that stress is avoided as much as possible and irritants are reduced), can exist.

Seaweed for Ulcers

Seaweed is a great healer of inflamed mucous membrane and guards against infection. Seaweed, together with slippery elm, is one of the quickest means of healing gastric and duodenal ulcers. A soothing concoction would be to make the slippery elm gruel with half milk and half carrageen moss liquid. No fruit juice would be added to the carrageen moss, as in the treatment of respiratory troubles. Honey should be added for its sweetening properties, though it also supplies energy and has healing properties of its own.

Carrageen moss, slippery elm and honey should be extensively used both in treating gastric and duodenal ulcers and in helping to avert them when there is a tendency to such conditions. Seaweed is a relaxant and helps reduce nervous tension. In this respect it is a valuable adjunct in the reduction of stress — and ulcers are a 'stress' condition. A late drink of the above mixture would be soothing to the gastric or duodenal ulceration and, at the same time, help to induce sleep. As in the case of respiratory troubles, a flask of the warm mixture could be kept at the bedside in case of any gnawing gastric pain or difficulty in sleeping. This type of drink should become a daily habit with those who have a nervous temperament.

Disease of any sort can never be prevented or conquered while the factors causing the disease still operate. Ulcers, therefore, can never be helped or avoided if no attempt is made to remove the causes. The daily use of seaweed in tablet or other form will always contribute to prevention of internal ulceration, but attention to correct nutrition is vital. Ulcers, however, have a tendency to recur if care is not taken, hence the daily use of seaweed is an added precaution.

CHAPTER NINE

GASTRIC CATARRH AND MUCOUS COLITIS

Both of the above troubles arise from irritation of mucous membrane and an excess of acidity. To this, of course, must be added a history of over-indulgence or lack of care in selecting essential foods. Practically all digestive troubles arise from over-feeding or eating wrong food. The troubles are then aggravated by tension, insufficient mastication, poor posture and by constipation and excessive smoking.

Gastric catarrh can only arise from an excess of mucus-forming foods, prolific use of condiments which irritate mucous membrane, chemicals contained in food and drink and, of course, many popular pain-killing drugs. Millions of pain-killing drugs and tranquillizers damage the system. Many of these drugs irritate the delicate mucous membranes of the body, damage the kidneys and cause internal haemorrhage.

Mucous colitis is also a catarrhal condition, where the mucous membranes of the colon are irritated. Males, who are more subject to tension than the average female, constitute the largest number of victims of gastric or duodenal ulcers. In the case of mucous colitis, however, it is the female sex who are the main sufferers. The clinical symptoms of mucous colitis are chronic constipation or constipation interspersed with periods of diarrhoea and the presence of mucus in the stools. The mucus may be in the form of clumps, strings or shreds, and considerable amounts may be passed.

Mucous colitis is more common amongst those with a weak constitution and who suffer from nervous tension and tend to aggravate (or even exaggerate) normal fears. It is for this latter reason that there is a tendency to use purgatives which act by irritating the mucous membrane of the colon. When the colon is irritated by the purging agent a forced bowel movement is the consequence. Irritation of the colon, however, merely adds to the cause of the mucous colitis and upsets the balance of the colon. The end result is to encourage a more severe constipation, punctuated by further attacks of diarrhoea.

The first need in the relief of gastric catarrh and mucous colitis is to reduce the irritation and inflammation of the mucous membrane. The diet, of course, has to be amended and irritation from purges must cease. Constipation must be tackled at its source — and this usually lies in the habit of eating too much white bread, white flour and white sugar products. White bread — and anything made from white flour — has had all natural roughage removed and is a well-known cause of constipation.

Seaweed Soothes Mucous Membrane

Seaweed soothes the delicate mucous membrane, provides a safe means of encouraging the muscular movements of the colon and combats constipation. One of the earliest purposes for which seaweed (agar-agar) was used by the Chinese and Japanese was for gastric-intestinal disorders. Seaweed is also antiseptic and guards against auto-intoxication which arises when chronic constipation exists. The advantage of seaweed is that while it supplies essential vitamins and mineral salts, it is also alkaline and cleansing and exerts a gentle laxative effect. It can, therefore, provide nutritional and therapeutic properties at one and the same time.

In the case of gastric catarrh and mucous colitis, seaweed should be taken both as a food supplement and used for making jellies, blancmanges and as a combined fruit and carrageen moss drink.

In the initial stages, in particular, seaweed should appear in jelly form, as a food supplement and as a drink at least twice in the day. When the worst symptoms of either diseased condition have definitely ceased, seaweed should still be a regular part of the diet. Quite frequently there is a predisposition to certain complaints, especially those with a catarrhal origin and the best defence against such a predisposition is to increase preventative measures. Seaweed is one simple means of both prevention and healing. Iodine deficiency is known to contribute to gastric trouble. Seaweed is a recognized source of iodine and has a high potassium content. Diarrhoea causes a high potassium loss which seaweed helps to replace.

CHAPTER TEN

GALL BLADDER DISEASE AND OBESITY

The gall bladder is a pear-shaped organ lying on the under surface of the liver and is a reservoir for bile. It is connected by ducts with the liver and the small intestine. Bile is an important digestive fluid (it also has an aperient action), and can be concentrated by the gall bladder. The gall bladder is lined by mucous membrane and is, therefore, very subject to catarrh. Gall bladder disease is often associated with obesity, chronic gastritis and constipation. Although stagnation in the gall bladder and irritation of its mucous membranes is conducive to the formation of gall stones, the disease can exist when no gall stones are present.

The same mucus-forming diet which causes catarrh elsewhere, also causes gall bladder trouble. When in addition to the subject of mucus-forming foods, there is an excess of high cholesterol foods — fried foods, fatty meat, cream, butter, eggs and cheese — gall stones can be readily formed.

The symptoms of gall bladder trouble are severe colic-type pains with nausea, vomiting and a sensation of fullness after meals. Heartburn, flatulence and waterbrash are also present. Obesity and lack of exercise are familiar features of gall bladder trouble.

Obesity has a detrimental effect on the entire system. Its influence on the gall bladder is mainly through pressure effects from the sagging abdomen and from the lack of exercise which obesity induces. The flow of bile is largely dependent upon the muscular movements of the diaphragm which take place in breathing. Obesity usually infers either over-eating or improper selection of food. The gall bladder, therefore, suffers from a variety of adverse circumstances when obesity is present. Not the least of these is the stagnation which occurs when the muscular movements in exercise and breathing are inadequate and bile is not expelled in sufficient quantities from the gall bladder. Inadequate expulsion of bile is one of the causes of constipation and stagnation in the gall bladder.

Formation of Gall Stones

'Fat, fair and forty' is the apt description of people who normally suffer from cholecystitis, a catarrhal condition of the gall-bladder and bile passages. Anything which impedes expulsion of bile favours the production of bile-sand from the pigments which are deposited in the gall bladder or bile ducts. The irritation caused by the bile sand aggravates the catarrhal condition. Eventually the bile sand collects into small masses and these masses are gradually encrusted with 'cholesterin' so that the progressively thickening layer forms quite large gall stones. This is especially the case when fatty foods are over-represented in the diet.

Obesity may not always produce either gall bladder trouble or gall stones. But obesity does favour the production of both, since the same factors are so often involved, especially in middle age and onwards, when physical activity decreases.

Diet and the avoidance of excess mucus and acid foods is essential to avoid catarrh and obesity. Mucous membrane is so extensive in the system that anything which avoids irritation of the membrane, or which reduces the excessive production of mucus, is bound to be of advantage to health.

Iodine for Energy

Iodine is the essential constituent of seaweed, which regulates metabolism and helps to counteract obesity. By increasing and regulating the metabolic rate, iodine supplies the physical and mental energy required for combating stagnation. Increase in energy automatically improves the physical activity that is essential to bile flow and shedding excess weight. Seaweed is also a liver cleanser. Anything that has a beneficial effect upon the liver must also exert a beneficial influence on the gall bladder.

Constipation almost always exists when the flow of bile is impeded. Seaweed again comes to the assistance of the body because it encourages peristaltis and has a laxative effect. However, one of the most important effects of seaweed is in its healing and soothing of irritated mucous membrane. Catarrh of the gall bladder can never be completely overcome while its mucous is the subject of irritation. Complete freedom from irritation is a difficult matter. Sensible diet, adequate exercise and diaphragmatic breathing stimulates the flow of bile, balances the weight and reduces the risk of constipation. The addition of seaweed to the diet can make the 'fat, fair and forty' description completely erroneous.

In all cases where there is even a tendency to the above description, seaweed should be used as a food supplement. Additional seaweed should be incorporated into the diet in the form of jellies, thickenings or as a carrageen moss drink flavoured with fruit juice.

CHAPTER ELEVEN

CONSTIPATION

Constipation is so common among sophisticated societies that it is almost accepted as a normal consequence of living. When, as in some cases, there is an exaggerated fear of not having a daily bowel movement, the condition is usually made worse by the adoption of purges which cause a chemical or mechanical irritant which compels a 'forced' defaecation. Artificial stimulus of this type damages the mucous membrane, alters the tone of the colon and aggravates the original condition. Constipation is usually caused by a combination of faulty diet in which there is a lack of natural roughage, vitamins and mineral salts; neglecting to respond to the natural desire for a bowel action; and by a colon which either absorbs water too rapidly or is what is termed 'spastic'. In the latter condition the muscle of the colon remains in a state of spasm. Lack of tone in the colon is often due to a deficiency of vitamin B_1 in the diet.

The white bread and white flour products, which are devoured in enormous quantities, are the arch enemies of a healthy colon. Such products are devoid of natural roughage and lack the vitamin and mineral content necessary to healthy existence. The colon requires bulk in a correct form to encourage peristaltic movements of the colon. Some bran in wheat is essential to bowel activity, but this is non-existent in ordinary white flour. While bran can be added to the diet to replace that taken from the wheat, this is not the ideal solution.

Natural Roughage
Natural roughage should be obtained from wholewheat bread, wholegrain cereals and from the fibrous matter of

fruit and vegetables. These foods also contain the vitamins and mineral salts which activate the gastric juices, ensure the flow of bile and promote muscular movements of the colon. Balance in food produces balance in colon activity.

Purges and laxatives which depend upon their irritant action in producing a bowel movement should be avoided at all costs. It is the use of these irritants which aggravate the initial condition and further the development of mucous colitis. Bowel movement should be restored by natural methods: diet, and more attention to the call for defaecation.

It will be recalled that a deficiency of B_1 is sometimes the cause of constipation. B_1 is present in many of the alkaline elements in diet, especially in raw fruit and salads. It is also found in milk, egg yolk, fish and lean meat. The body is unable to store vitamin B_1 for any period of time, so it must be included in sufficient quantities in the normal daily diet. Daily seaweed tablets help to ensure that the vitamin is contained in the diet.

Auto-intoxication

Constipation inevitably produces some degree of auto-intoxication. Seaweed combats auto-intoxication in four ways:

1. The high mineral salt content builds up and tones the walls of the colon and encourages muscular movement in the colon.
2. The same mineral salts are alkaline and counteract acidity.
3. The iodine content of seaweed is highly antiseptic.
4. It forms an excellent lubricant for assisting defaecation.

Seaweed, in either the form of agar-agar or carrageen moss, is highly recommended as a prophylactic or for direct therapeutic use in the treatment of constipation. Agar-agar can be sprinkled over food or can be used for making sweet or savoury jellies or as a thickening agent. Agar-agar, like carrageen moss, can be purchased in a triturated form. Agar-agar is more suitable for direct use on food, but both can be utilized for jellies, or thickening of soups or drinks.

With the ideal diet — a balanced and largely lactovegetarian diet with at least 60 per cent of fruit and vegetables and using wholegrain cereals and wholewheat bread — constipation should not exist. There is no reason why fish and a moderate amount of lean meat should not be included in the diet. The facts indicate that nature places everything at our disposal to ensure normal bowel functioning. For reasons of ignorance, convenience or financial exploitation, however, scant attention is given to making the best employment of natural resources.

Seaweed a 'Safe' Laxative

It is difficult to avoid some of the faults that exist in modern nutrition. Constipation can be avoided if the diet is amended to include sufficient of the alkaline fruits and vegetables (especially raw salads and raw fruit), to provide natural roughage and the best type of liquid for the bowel. As an additional safeguard, however, seaweed, either as a food supplement or direct food, should be taken daily. Seaweed is the 'safe' laxative. But over and above that it is also a direct source of essential vitamins and mineral salts which guard against disease.

CHAPTER TWELVE

INTESTINAL DISORDERS

Intestinal disorders which respond to seaweed include diarrhoea, dysentry and tapeworms.

Diarrhoea, of course, is the most common of the above complaints. But diarrhoea — looseness of the bowels — is really a symptom of disease. Catarrhal diarrhoea is the more normal form of the disorder and is caused by the swelling and inflammation of the mucous membrane of the intestines. Diarrhoea, however, is often caused by the excessive use of purges and from toxic agents in food. The looseness of the bowels is due to the need to expel extraneous or toxic matter and is nature's way of relieving congestion.

Chronic constipation will cause diarrhoea, because hard and impacted faecal matter irritates the membranes. Any form of irritant — toxic drugs, poisons in food and even a sudden excess of certain summer fruits (peaches, apricots) — may cause looseness of the bowels. Sudden heat spells can also bring on an attack of diarrhoea.

In most cases diarrhoea is a short, salutary lesson in nature's attempts to cleanse the body. Repeated diarrhoea, however, can be a symptom of more serious trouble and should never be neglected. In certain cases, as in dysentery, for instance, the severity of the disease can be gauged by the extent of the diarrhoea.

Carrageen Moss for Diarrhoea

Seaweed is a laxative, yet it is also advised in the case of diarrhoea. Carrageen moss can and should be used for the treatment of diarrhoea. Seaweed is known to strengthen, tone and lubricate the alimentary canal. Furthermore, it is a valuable antiseptic. In a sense, therefore, seaweed is a balancer and healer of the colon.

Dysentery is rarely found in Western civilizations but it does occur from time to time, especially in a mild form when abdominal colic is followed by diarrhoea and some fever. In very mild cases there may only be catarrh of the intestine with an excessive excretion of mucus matter. Seaweed, in the form of carrageen moss, should be liberally taken in any discomfort that is associated with diarrhoea, dysentery or any other condition where the mucous membranes of the intestines are suffering from congestion and irritation. The presence of excess mucus in stools, or looseness of the bowels, is an obvious indication of intestinal irritation which demands the immediate healing and antiseptic qualities of seaweed.

Vermifuge is the name given to any agent that will expel worms from the intestine. Some specimens of seaweed have long been used for this purpose in places as far apart as Greece and Turkey to China and Japan. In Japan it is a red seaweed, *Digena simplex*, that is principally used and other red species of seaweed are employed in the Mediterranean areas. But green and brown seaweeds are also known to act as vermifuges. The Maoris of New Zealand use bull kelp, *Durvillea*, a brown seaweed, for the treatment of worms.

Garlic has the highest iodine content of any land plant and it is also a valuable antiseptic. Garlic is also an excellent vermifuge, but it has some disadvantages in that, while it is excellent for catarrhal conditions, it can irritate the kidneys and be over-stimulating to the gastric organs. Seaweed is essentially healing and balancing and is, therefore, especially suitable for children who may suffer from diarrhoea or worms. It is also more palatable to most, especially young children.

One of the main advantages of seaweed is that it can be given in so many pleasant forms. Apart from slightly disguising the flavour with either fruit juices or savoury mixtures, there is no reaon why it should not appear on the table as anything but a pleasant food or drink. What is always important to bear in mind, however, is that seaweed can be taken as a food supplement to prevent onsets of disease.

CHAPTER THIRTEEN

GENITO-URINARY AND REPRODUCTIVE SYSTEMS

For many decades the Japanese, Chinese and Malayan nationals have been using seaweed for disorders connected with both the genito-urinary tract and reproductive system. The common ailments which come under the above heading include malfunction of the kidneys, bladder weakness or cystitis, enlargement of the prostate gland, disease of the uterus (causing menstrual disorders), and ovarian troubles.

Variety of Mineral Salts

There are various reasons why seaweed is valuable to the genito-urinary and reproductive systems. The genito-urinary tract is partly lined with mucous membrane and suffers, like mucous membrane elsewhere in the body, from irritation and inflammation. Apart from soothing and healing such irritation, seaweed provides a great variety of mineral salts which enrich and activate the tissues and cleanse the bloodstream. A pure bloodstream is not only a guarantee of balanced nutrition, it also means an efficient interchange and elimination of waste matter, thus preventing stagnation and congestion.

It is an established fact that seaweed has a normalizing and remedial action on the arteries, liver, kidneys, gall bladder, pancreas, prostate gland, testicles, uterus and ovaries. This is additional to its healing action on irritated mucous membrane and muscular movements. Seaweed eases tension by its action on the sensory nerves and is a natural tranquillizer. Seaweed supplies phosphorus, potassium, sodium and iron — all mineral salts which are essential to the building of sound nerves. The elements: lead, copper, silver and zinc are also contained in seaweed.

It is deficiency of these mineral salts and elements — which should come from natural food resources — that is often the cause of a weak nervous system. Menstrual and ovarian disorders are often either the cause, or are associated with, nervous tension, depression and headaches.

Over and above this, however, it is the high iodine content of seaweed that makes it essential to the health of the thyroid gland. The thyroid gland is one of the most important glands in the endocrine system and assists in the balanced function of that system. Any disturbance or deficiency in the thyroid affects the entire system — hence its importance to the sex glands.

A Clean Bloodstream

Seaweed has been found useful in treating enlarged prostate, impotence, irregular menstruation and for toning a weak uterus. The healing effect is not merely in helping to regulate the endocrine system, but also in the fact that seaweed is of direct nutritional value and ensures that a clean bloodstream is constantly circulating through the tissues.

Seaweed in the form of a food supplement is strongly recommended for all the above conditions. Where enlargement of the prostate glad is concerned, the diet should also be reinforced by taking pumpkin seeds daily. The best type of seaweed is carrageen moss in the form of drinks and jellies. Needless to say, there is an absolute necessity for a balanced diet to ensure full and correct nutrition in whatever form of complaint. It is only by strengthening the resistance to disease that the body can maintain health. The advantage of seaweed, however, is that it is a natural food and should be included in any diet.

CHAPTER FOURTEEN

MUSCULO-SKELETAL AND NEURO-MUSCULAR SYSTEMS

Rheumatism and allied diseases are among the scourges of mankind. Environment, occupation, habits and accidents play some part in deciding which type of disease is suffered in the muscular-skeletal and neuro-muscular systems. Climate plays a lesser role in the above complaints than is generally recognized. What must be taken into account, however, is that, apart from such predisposing factors as occupation, hereditary influences, fatigue, abuse and environment, there must be some larger cause for the high incidence of rheumatism, arthritis, fibrositis and similar ailments.

Defective Nutrition

The answer, to a very great extent, must be defective nutrition, since food is the one common denominator. Imbalance in nutrition must cause imbalance in health. A gross deficiency in one particular vitamin, mineral or hormone is soon reflected in the body. The lack of iodine for the thyroid gland, for instance, is a classic example. Gross deficiencies are recognized early. But a great deal of disease is caused by a persistently low supply of the protective elements. This deficiency, while lowering resistance to disease, is not recognized as a nutritional problem. A great deal of early degeneration — as in arthritis or high blood pressure, etc. — is due to long-standing nutritional deficiencies.

The other factor in nutrition is the excess of acid-forming foods in the average diet. In most ailments of the category being considered, from rheumatism to fibrositis and neuritis, an excess of acids is always present. This is much the same whether it is the uric acid in rheumatism or whether it is the acidity and lack of protective elements which cause inflammation of the nerve or nerve sheath in neuritis. In all diseases of the musculo-skeletal and neuro-muscular systems there is a very large element of impure bloodstream, defective circulation in and around the joints and tissues and excess of acidity.

Iodine a Tranquillizer

One factor in disease that tends to be overlooked is that while stress and fatigue can cause disease, disease itself, especially in painful joints and the boring and burning pain of neuritis, for instance, can create stress and fatigue. Painful diseases, therefore, aggravate discomfort and set up a vicious circle. Iodine is a natural tranquillizer and helps to reduce nervous tension, and seaweed is the most natural source of iodine.

Drugs may alleviate pain. Indeed there is a too ready recourse to drugs for even the simplest malady. What is overlooked, however, is that all drugs are toxic and their side-effects add to the debilitation of the system. At some time or other the body will react or chronic disease sets in.

In all diseases of the musculo-skeletal system there is a need for mobility. Pain frequently restricts mobility. Pain, however, is a reminder that a diseased condition exists and is, therefore, a somewhat necessary evil. Dulling pain does not necessarily cure the disease. The tremendous sale of drugs is not only a constant reminder that disease abounds, it is also a reminder that the cure does not lie in drugs. Excessive drug-taking is a source of many authoritative misgivings. This is more particularly so since many diseases and obscure ailments are the result of drug-taking.

Neuritis is a very painful affliction and, while drugs relieve the pain, they are not the complete answer. Drugs do not supply the essential vitamins and mineral salts which are required to nourish the nerves. Drugs do not reduce the acids which cause rheumatism, in fact they add to that store of acidity. More fundamental is the need to provide the correct nutrient, improve the blood supply and reduce stagnation from accumulated waste matter.

Seaweed Protects Against Disease
Balanced diet is vital to health. But with modern food technology even the best diet may suffer some deficiencies. To ensure that the deficiencies are avoided, some food supplements are almost essential. Seaweed is one such food supplement and helps to provide protection against disease. In diseases of the neuro-muscular system such as neuritis, vitamin B_{12} should also be included. In all cases, however, seaweed should be taken as a normal part of diet in the manner previously indicated.

Extract of Seaweed
The use of seaweed is not limited to the actual ingestion of that versatile commodity. Extract of seaweed makes a valuable addition to a bath for the relief of all rheumatic pains. An extract from seaweed is usually dark-brownish in colour. While this extract has been used therapeutically for many years in the treatment of all types of ailments, it is only in the last few years that its use has become more widespread. When the extract is used in a bath for the treatment of rheumatism, muscle or joint pains, the bath can be quite hot (always terminated by a cold shower or spray), but when it is used for the treatment of neuritis extreme heat must be avoided and the bath should be tepid.

CHAPTER FIFTEEN

OTHER USES

It is not suggested that seaweed is a miracle worker. What is suggested, however, is that for too many years seaweed, virtually the oldest plant in the universe, has been neglected.

Seaweed is an anti-coagulant. Seaweeds differ in their various properties according to location and season when gathered. Carrageen moss is an anti-coagulant. In the case of the carrageen variety it is the seaweed *Chondrus* which contains the anti-coagulant, but it must be gathered at the correct time. Other groups possess this quality, including a red seaweed called *Delesseria sanguinea*.

All edible seaweeds, by promoting the function of the parathyroid glands, ensure that the mineral salts supplied by food (including seaweed) are absorbed and assimilated to the best advantage. Calcium, iodine and sodium all play a particular part in maintaining the tone and elasticity of the arterial walls. Seaweed is also a blood-cleanser. A combination of factors, therefore, makes seaweed extremely useful in the treatment of high blood-pressure. The condition may be a result of stress, impure bloodstream or hardening of the arteries. Often it is a combination of these factors. Seaweed has a beneficial effect upon all the causes mentioned.

Seaweed for Stress

Stress, like impoverished and denatured food, is a permanent feature of modern life. Stress is one of the main causes of psychosomatic ailments — asthma and peptic ulcer are examples. It is all the more important to combat such features of life with correct and adequate nutrition. Seaweed contains all the essentials for protection against the effects of stress and, since it is a completely natural food, provides them in the most easily assimilated form.

Mention has been made of using an extract of seaweed in baths for the relief of pain and in the treatment of disease. An extract of seaweed is not absolutely necessary. It can be used in its original form by being left to soak overnight and then pouring the seaweed water into the bath. Packets of seaweed are available for this purpose. The external uses of seaweed are listed below.

Obesity	Hot seaweed bath followed by a cold shower.
Bronchitis and respiratory troubles	,,
Rheumatism and allied complaints	,,
Digestive and genito-urinary disorders	,,
Hypertension, insomnia, nervous debility and tension, skin diseases, burns, insect bites	Prolonged *tepid* seaweed bath (not over 100° Fahr. for 15 to 30 minutes)

The fluid extract of seaweed can be applied to unbroken skin in the treatment of sprains and bruises. Dried seaweed powder can be mixed with vaseline or wheat germ oil and used as an embrocation for the treatment of swollen, painful and stiff joints.

Seaweed the Great Balancer

Few plants are blessed with the versatility of seaweed. The infinite applications and high nutriment value of this age-old plant makes it an important addition to the food resources and therapeutic agents available to man. *Seaweed is the great balancer.*

As yet, the total supply of edible seaweed is virtually untapped. There is no doubt that greater use will be made of the food resources the seas are capable of supplying. Seaweed is one of these resources. The dangers of sea pollution have been recognized and acted upon. With reasonable care such food sources will soon be virtually uncontaminated and seaweed remains one of the most natural and unspoilt foods available.

The dangers of man's interference with natural food is not yet fully appreciated. By supplying essential protein vitamins and mineral salts in a completely natural state, seaweed is in advance of most present-day foods and this is a factor of ever-growing importance.

For better health and happier living.

THE VITAMINS EXPLAINED SIMPLY

Vitamins are chemical compounds which, with minor exceptions, cannot be made in the body, but come from food. Without vitamins neither normal development nor health is possible. Last century food contained all man's nutritional requirements; today the vitamin content of food is dangerously diminished by processing and chemical additives. This book reveals what ailments vitamins prevent and remedy and gives estimated daily requirements of each vitamin.

LIVER AILMENTS AND COMMON DISORDERS

This book provides dietary recommendations and detailed vitamin dosage for such liver ailments as migraine, kidney and bladder troubles, glandular disturbances, enlarged tonsils and adenoids, goitre, anaemia, underweight, unhealthy hair, varicose veins and ulcers. The liver is a vital organ and functions as the body's chemical laboratory; producing bile (which makes food alkaline) is one of its functions.

IMPROVE YOUR SIGHT WITHOUT GLASSES

Demolishes a long-cherished belief that the only remedy for refractory eye troubles is spectacles. In fact this book demonstrates that eye troubles can be eliminated and sight tremendously improved by a simple combination of exercises and dietary measures, without using spectacles — which are merely 'crutches'. Also gives treatment for cataract, conjunctivitis and glaucoma, and explains hyperimetropia (far sight) and myopia (short sight).

RHEUMATISM AND ARTHRITIS

Explains the main rheumatic categories of rheumatoid arthritis, osteo-arthritis, lumbago, neuritis, sciatica, gout, spondylitis, bursitis and rheumatic fever; causes of rheumatic ailments; the injurious side effects of orthodox therapies; with advice on applying natural remedial principles and the sweat therapy. Gives hope to all rheumatic and arthritic sufferers.